Code-IT Primary Programming

Coding Workbook 3
Algorithm to Code

A complete Computer Science study programme for Key Stage 2 using the free programming language Scratch

Phil Bagge

First published in Great Britain in 2015 by
The University of Buckingham Press
Yeomanry House
Hunter Street
Buckingham MK18 1EG

ISBN 9781908684561

Contents

How to use this book

Your teacher will instruct you when to use these resources. Please don't complete them until asked.

Each Scratch programming project has an overview page with further challenges that you can try at home.

One star challenges are the easiest and three star challenges are the hardest.

Remember in school it is your responsibility to fix/debug your own code and that is true at home as well. No one learns anything by having someone else do it for them!

• If you get stuck you may want to try some of these strategies:

• Read the code out loud. Does it make sense?

• Explain the code to a favourite stuffed toy. (This is called rubber ducking).

• Click on just one block of code: does it do what you think it should? If it does move on and try another block until you find the bug.

• Save your work first. Break long code into smaller sections. Test each block separately. This is called divide and conquer.

Remember even professional programmers get stuck sometimes and have to find and fix bugs. This is normal and will help you become a more resilient problem solver.

You don't have to just stick to these challenges: if you spot something you want to create, go for it.

Bug = error in programming

Debugging = finding and fixing bugs

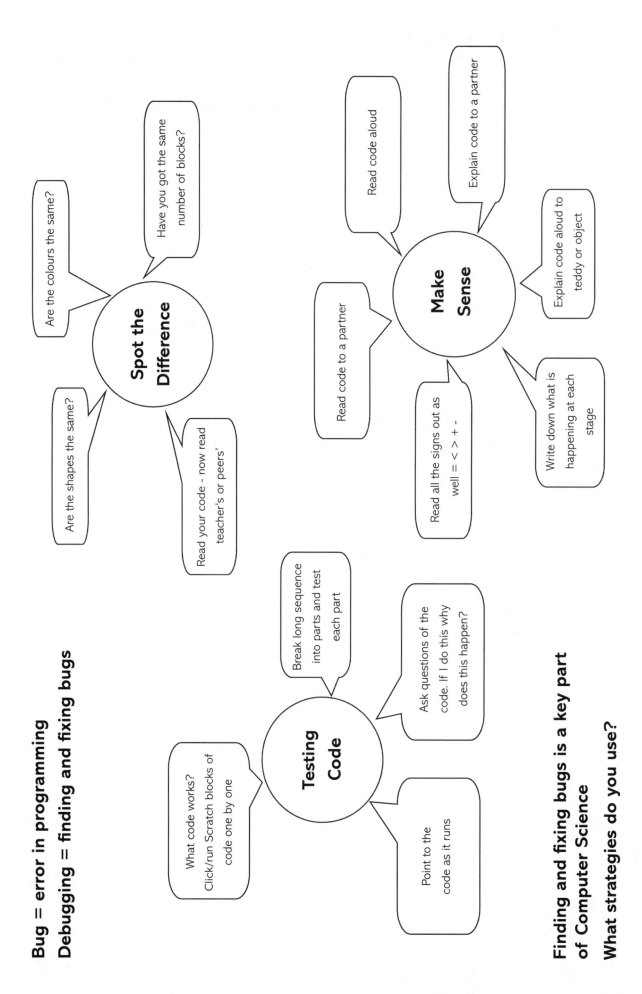

Spot the Difference

- Are the colours the same?
- Have you got the same number of blocks?
- Are the shapes the same?
- Read your code - now read teacher's or peers'

Make Sense

- Read code aloud
- Explain code to a partner
- Explain code aloud to teddy or object
- Read code to a partner
- Read all the signs out as well = < > + -
- Write down what is happening at each stage

Testing Code

- Break long sequence into parts and test each part
- Ask questions of the code. If I do this why does this happen?
- What code works? Click/run Scratch blocks of code one by one
- Point to the code as it runs

Finding and fixing bugs is a key part of Computer Science

What strategies do you use?

3ᴀ. Counting Machine

Create a program that can count to any number.

Computational Thinking

Algorithm & Programming Evaluation

In this module we will discover that there are many ways to do the same
task but that not all solutions are of equal value; some are better, more
efficient, quicker, more easily adapted and use less code.

Computational Doing

Variables

Variables are like pots that store things for you. You can set the variable
which is like emptying it out and putting whatever you want inside. Or you
can change the variable which allows you to add or take away from what is
already inside the variable.

Challenge Yourself At Home

Ask a parent or guardian if you can either download Scratch 2.0 https://scratch.mit.edu/scratch2download/ and
install it on your computer or use the online version available here https://scratch.mit.edu/.
On the iPad download Pyonkee.

First Steps	☆	Adapt the timer to create a times tables counter to help younger children learn their tables.
Next Steps	☆ ☆	Can the times tables user choose which table to learn?
Further Steps	☆ ☆ ☆	Find a program you have created in the past such as a quiz and add a timer. Can you integrate the timer into the program so that it triggers something? It doesn't have to end the program but it could.

Describe your project here

What did you enjoy doing? Did you discover any new effects? Did you struggle with anything? Remember all
programmers make mistakes (bugs) and the best ones keep trying to find a way to fix things!

_____

_____

_____

_____

_____

_____

Learning Intention:

I am learning to create, adapt, evaluate and improve a counting machine.

Success Criteria:	How did I do?		
I discovered a simple way to make the cat count	◯	◯	◯
I adapted my simple method to include a variable and a loop	◯	◯	◯
I followed the flowchart to build a counting program	◯	◯	◯
I created a 30 seconds countdown timer	◯	◯	◯
I created a countdown timer where the user input the length of time in seconds	◯	◯	◯
I fed the user answer back to them using the say command	◯	◯	◯
I added a timer to my maths quiz	◯	◯	◯
	wk1	wk2	wk3

☺ I can do it

😐 I did it a bit but didn't fully get it

☹ I didn't get it at all

Teacher use only

◯ ◯ ◯

Match the Scratch blocks to the flowchart by drawing lines to them

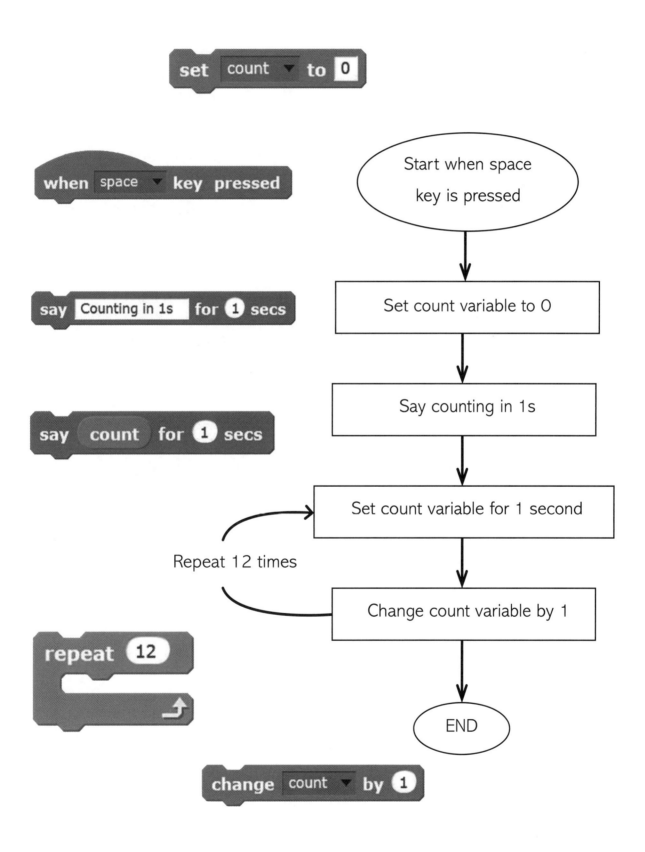

Tick the two blocks that get repeated 12 times

Tick the challenges that you coded and checked with your teacher

	Challenges	
	Count faster	
	Count in 2s	
	Count in 7s	
	Count backwards	
	Count in halves	
	Count in tenths	
	Count in hundredths	
	Start from 30	
	Start from -60	
	Start from 100 count backwards in 8s	

3B. Music Abstraction

Convert a music track into Scratch code using abstraction to help.

Computational Thinking

Abstraction is the skill of reducing complexity by hiding irrelevant detail and focussing on the most important element. In this module we will use abstraction to determine which elements of a music video are useful.

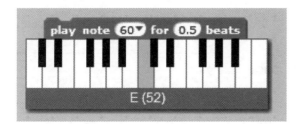

Challenge Yourself At Home

Ask a parent or guardian if you can either download Scratch 2.0 https://scratch.mit.edu/scratch2download/ and install it on your computer or use the online version available here https://scratch.mit.edu/.
On the iPad download Pyonkee.

First Steps Can you think of any other times that you have needed to use the skill of abstraction? For instance where stripping away less useful facts and concentrating on the most important elements has been useful?

Next Steps ☆ ☆ Can you use abstraction to reduce the key learning in this lesson to one of two statements? Or can you abstract another music track of your choice and convert it into Scratch code?

Further Steps ☆ ☆ ☆ The computer treats each note as a number. Can you work out a way to play music using a number inside a variable?

Describe your project here

What did you enjoy doing? Did you discover any new effects? Did you struggle with anything? Remember all programmers make mistakes (bugs) and the best ones keep trying to find a way to fix things!

_____

_____

_____

_____

_____

_____

_____

Learning Intention:

I am learning to turn music into Scratch code using the skill of abstraction.

Success Criteria:	How did I do?		
I can identify all the different elements in the track	○	○	○
I can use abstraction to remove unwanted detail from the track	○	○	○
I can create an algorithm of the track based on pitch and length of note	○	○	○
I can convert my musical algorithm into Scratch code and test it	○	○	○
I can refine my code to make it closer to the original track	○	○	○
I can spot and fix (debug) errors in my code	○	○	○
	wk1	wk2	wk3

☺ I can do it

😐 I did it a bit but didn't fully get it

☹ I didn't get it at all

Teacher use only

○   ○   ○

Baa Baa Black Sheep Break It Down

List all the elements on the video/song

1		
2		
3		
4		
5		
6		
7		

Tick the elements that you need to turn the music into Scratch musical notes.

Abstraction Definition

Abstraction is the skill of reducing complexity by hiding irrelevant detail and focussing on the most important element.

Music Abstraction Algorithm Notation Sheet

3c. Random Word

Create a program that generates words or phrases.

Computational Thinking

Generalisation adapts a solution to make it do something else. In this module we will learn how to create and use a list and then you will use generalisation to make it do something similar but different.

Computational Doing

Lists

Lists can store numbers and words. They are different from variables because they are ordered one after the other, just like a shopping list. In this module we will be creating lists and then choosing random items from the list.

Other programming languages sometimes call lists arrays or tables.

Challenge Yourself At Home

Ask a parent or guardian if you can either download Scratch 2.0 https://scratch.mit.edu/scratch2download/ and install it on your computer or use the online version available here https://scratch.mit.edu/.
On the iPad download Pyonkee.

First Steps Create your own project that uses randomly chosen elements from lists. It could be an I'm bored activity chooser for yourself or a younger member of your family, a way of choosing an excuse to avoid something or a fun idea of your own.

Next Steps Can you find a way to get the program user to add something to the list without having to use the + sign on the list?

Further Steps Can you find a way to get the computer to respond if a specific choice on your list is chosen? Hint: you may need a variable and a selection block.

Describe your project here

What did you enjoy doing? Did you discover any new effects? Did you struggle with anything? Remember all programmers make mistakes (bugs) and the best ones keep trying to find a way to fix things!

_____

_____

_____

_____

_____

_____

Learning Intention:

I am learning to use lists to randomise elements

Success Criteria:	How did I do?		
I can create lists	○	○	○
I can add and delete items from a list	○	○	○
I can explain how a random element can be chosen from a list	○	○	○
I would like to use a list to create a program that...			
I can spot and fix (debug) errors in my code	○	○	○
	wk1	wk2	wk3

☺ I can do it

😐 I did it a bit but didn't fully get it

☹ I didn't get it at all

Teacher use only

○ ○ ○

3D. Coin Sorter

Changing any amount into the least coins.

Computational Thinking

Pattern Recognition: In this module we are going to investigate the least amount of coins an amount can be split into. We are going to look for the repeating pattern in the algorithm.

Computational Doing

Repeat Until Scratch Block

This block is a member of the loop or repetition family. Instead of repeating a certain number of times or repeating forever it repeats until a condition is met.

Repeat until Learnt song

Learn words
Listen to tune
Sing words

Challenge Yourself At Home

Ask a parent or guardian if you can either download Scratch 2.0 https://scratch.mit.edu/scratch2download/ and install it on your computer or use the online version available here https://scratch.mit.edu/.
On the iPad download Pyonkee.

First Steps ☆ Can you write a quiz question which asks the user to write a number less than or greater than another number?

Next Steps ☆☆ Can you use the repeat until block to stop a moving sprite if it touches the mouse pointer or alternatively a colour on the background or if a key is pressed?

Further Steps ☆☆☆ Can you find other ways to use the repeat until block?

Describe your project here

What did you enjoy doing? Did you discover any new effects? Did you struggle with anything? Remember all programmers make mistakes (bugs) and the best ones keep trying to find a way to fix things!

_____

_____

_____

_____

_____

_____

_____

Learning Intention:

I am learning to spot patterns and convert a flowchart algorithm into code.

Success Criteria:	How did I do?	
I can investigate greater than and less than using Scratch	◯	◯
I can work out how to check for = as well as greater than and less than independently	◯	◯
I can spot the flowchart pattern and fill in the missing blocks	◯	◯
I can match the flowchart algorithm to the blocks correctly	◯	◯
I spotted where one flowchart block was converted into two Scratch blocks	◯	◯
I can build and test my change machine using £2 and £1 coins	◯	◯
I can complete the program using all other coins	◯	◯
I can add in notes	◯	◯
I can explain what is happening in the program in detail on video or using the comments	◯	◯
I can convert this program to work with pre-decimal currency	◯	◯
I can adapt the program to work with currencies other than sterling (pounds and pence)	◯	◯
I can explain where this program might be useful	◯	◯
I can make the program repeat automatically	◯	◯
Challenge I can debug (spot and fix) any errors	◯	◯
	wk1	wk2

☺ I can do it

😐 I did it a bit but didn't fully get it

☹ I didn't get it at all

Teacher use only

◯ ◯

Coin Sorter Write in what should go in the empty flowchart shapes.
Draw lines to connect the flow chart algorithm with the code blocks

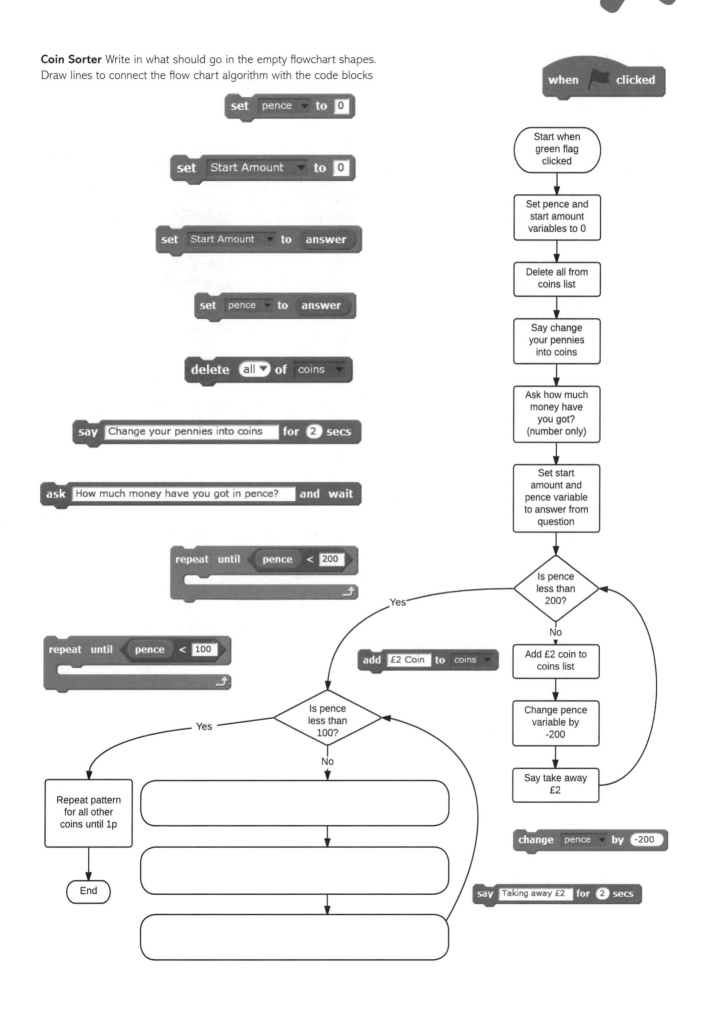

3E. Crab Maze

Create a Crab Maze game. Avoid the walls and reach the ends of the maze to move up a level.

Computational Thinking

Decomposition Before you start to build this project you will need to decompose it carefully. Ask yourself what are all the objects you will need to make and what will you need to make them do?

Computational Doing

X and Y Coordinate Blocks

You will be using coordinate blocks to move the Crab Sprite back to the beginning at the start of the game and when the end of each level is reached.

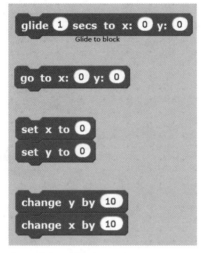

Coordinate Blocks

Challenge Yourself At Home

Ask a parent or guardian if you can either download Scratch 2.0 https://scratch.mit.edu/scratch2download/ and install it on your computer or use the online version available here https://scratch.mit.edu/.
On the iPad download Pyonkee.

First Steps ☆		When you move the sprite to a new place on the stage the coordinates change. Move the sprite to a new position then grab a glide to block. Repeat this lots of times. Run the code. How could you use this in your own creations?
Next Steps ☆ ☆		Put a change y by 1 block inside a forever loop. Experiment with positive and negative numbers - what happens? Try a change y and a change x block in the same forever loop. Can you work out how to move diagonally?
Further Steps ☆ ☆ ☆		Could you make a sprite move using a variable inside an x or y block?

Describe your project here

What did you enjoy doing? Did you discover any new effects? Did you struggle with anything? Remember all programmers make mistakes (bugs) and the best ones keep trying to find a way to fix things!

_____

_____

_____

_____

_____

_____

Learning Intention: I am learning to decompose a game independently before creating my own version in Scratch

Success Criteria:	How did I do?			
I decomposed all the elements that I would need to create	○	○	○	○
I decomposed all the things the crab would need to do	○	○	○	○
I decomposed all the elements the coins would need to do	○	○	○	○
I can make my crab look like it is opening and closing its claws	○	○	○	○
I can make my crab move when the game starts	○	○	○	○
I can make my crab steer when I press a key on the keyboard	○	○	○	○
I can design mazes with starts and finishes	○	○	○	○
I can make mazes with starts and finishes where all the walls are the same colour	○	○	○	○
I can make the game stop when the crab touches the maze wall	○	○	○	○
I can make a spawn point so the crab starts at the starting point	○	○	○	○
I can fix (debug) any errors	○	○	○	○
Extension	○	○	○	○
I can make the game change level when the crab touches a colour	○	○	○	○
I can make a coin that can be picked up by the crab increasing his score	○	○	○	○
I improved the game by adding my own element which did…	○	○	○	○
Challenge: How might I make or adapt a game like this myself?	wk1	wk2	wk3	wk4

☺ I can do it

😐 Did it a bit but didn't fully get it

☹ Didn't get it at all

Teacher use only
○ ○ ○ ○

What do you need to make the crab do?

What do you need to make the coins do?

What do you need to make the crab do when it reaches the finish?

What objects do you need to make?

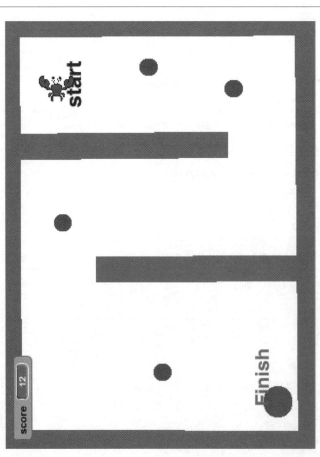

What would you add to make the games even better?

Decompose Crab Game

3F. Toilet Fan

Build a fan out of Lego and then program it.

Computational Thinking

Algorithm Evaluation and Generalisation

When programming there is always more than one way to achieve the same outcome. Look out for methods that use less code (algorithm evaluation) or that could be more easily used to achieve similar things (generalisation).

Computational Doing

Programming is used to control motors, lights, sounds and other physical outputs. You will program a single motor in today's project and use a distance sensor input. A computer can be used to work with very complex machinery that controls multiple outputs responding to many inputs. The race is on for a fully automated road-safe car.

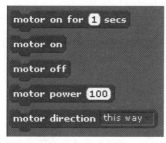

Motor blocks

Challenge Yourself At Home

First Steps ☆ A traffic light is a set of light outputs that are programmed to work in the same sequence every time they are used. How are traffic lights triggered? Hint- there are at least three ways.

Next Steps ☆ ☆ An automated shop door is programmed to open when it senses customers approaching. What safety features will the programmers need to build into their design?

Further Steps ☆ ☆ ☆ Can you list any other motors, lights or sound objects in the real world that could be controlled by a simple program?

_____

_____

_____

_____

_____

_____

_____

Learning Intention:

I am learning to build and code a fan using Lego Wedo and Scratch.

Success Criteria:	How did I do?	
I can design and build a model fan with distance sensor out of Lego WeDo (it doesn't have to draw or blow air)	◯	◯
I can code the fan to turn on (using the **o key**) and off (using the **x key**) using keyboard buttons	◯	◯
I can code the fan to go at fast (using the **f key**) slow (using the **s key**) and medium (using the **m key**) speeds	◯	◯
I can code the fan to turn on, spin for a set time and then turn off again (using the **t key**)	◯	◯
I can code the fan to start slowly and gradually get faster before gradually getting slower again (triggered by the **r key**)	◯	◯
Extension	◯	◯
I can code the fan to speed up using a variable	◯	◯
I can code the fan to start when it detects movement within 50mm and stop when outside that distance	◯	◯
Challenge I can debug (spot and fix) any errors	◯	◯
	wk1	wk2

☺ I can do it

😐 Did it a bit but didn't fully get it

☹ Didn't get it at all

Teacher use only

◯ ◯

36. Car Park Barrier

Build a barrier out of Lego and then program it.

Computational Thinking

Decomposition

The challenge is to program the car park barrier to sense a car approaching, raise the barrier, wait for the car to enter and then close the barrier. You can write a new program for this or you can use many of the elements that have solved problems for you before - such as raising the barrier and lowering the barrier. This is decomposition in action as you split up the complex task into smaller tasks and solve them separately.

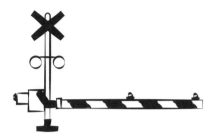

Challenge Yourself At Home

Challenge

Can you write an algorithm to operate a train level crossing-barrier? There are two barriers that block the road when the train crosses it. There can also be audible sirens and flashing lights. How would you trigger these? If someone is stuck on the line how can the train be stopped?

_____

_____

_____

_____

_____

_____

_____

_____

_____

_____

_____

_____

Learning Intention:

I am learning to design, build and program a Car Park barrier

Building Success Criteria:	How did I do?	
I can design and build a barrier out of Lego using a motor and a distance sensor	◯	◯
I can place the distance sensor so it would detect the car approaching the barrier	◯	◯
I can stop my barrier hitting things behind it	◯	◯
Programming Success Criteria:		
I can program an emergency cut off switch when the **space** key is pressed	◯	◯
I can program my barrier to rise **slowly** when the **r** key is pressed	◯	◯
I can program my barrier to lower **slowly** when the **l** key is pressed	◯	◯
I can program my barrier to make a warning sound before and during the barrier movement	◯	◯
Programming Extension Criteria:		
I can program my barrier to rise when the distance sensor detects a car within 50mm of the barrier, wait 5 seconds for the car to enter and then lower slowly	◯	◯
	wk1	wk2

What is the design fault with the distance sensor model and how could you fix it if you had more Lego? (Answer this with your partner)

_____

_____

☺ I can do it

😐 I did it a bit but didn't fully get it

☹ I didn't get it at all

Teacher use only

◯ ◯

3H. Angle Menu

Write a program that names the Angle.

Computational Thinking

Algorithm

Identify angles and list them by their properties. You can then use this as your algorithm before converting it into code to name the angle.

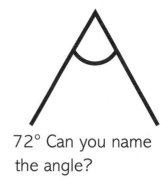

72° Can you name the angle?

Challenge Yourself At Home

Ask a parent or guardian if you can either download Scratch 2.0 https://scratch.mit.edu/scratch2download/ and install it on your computer or use the online version available here https://scratch.mit.edu/.
On the iPad download Pyonkee.

First Steps Can you get the computer to draw the angle after the user has inputed it?

Next Steps Can you get the computer to draw a snowflake pattern?

Further Steps Can you write a program that allows the user to guess the number the computer generated randomly? You may want to keep the range of possible numbers very small to start with.

pick random **1** to **10**

Describe your project here

What did you enjoy doing? Did you discover any new effects? Did you struggle with anything? Remember all programmers make mistakes (bugs) and the best ones keep trying to find a way to fix things!

_____

_____

_____

_____

_____

_____

_____

Learning Intention:

I am learning to create an algorithm for Angle Types before converting this into Scratch code.

Success Criteria: Main path bold	How did I do?	
Using two conditions can save time and use less code because...		
I can add code using an **AND** that works out if you are at junior or secondary school	◯	◯
The difference between **AND OR** is...		
I can order the angle algorithm correctly	◯	◯
I can convert the angle algorithm into Scratch code	◯	◯
I can debug (spot and fix) any errors	◯	◯
I can draw the angle (extension activity)	◯	◯
Challenge I can explain how this program might be useful elsewhere	◯	◯
	wk1	wk2

☺ I can do it

😐 I did it a bit but didn't fully get it

☹ I didn't get it at all

Teacher use only
◯ ◯

Angle Types Algorithm

Read the angle information below and then fill in the chart in order. The first two have been done for you.

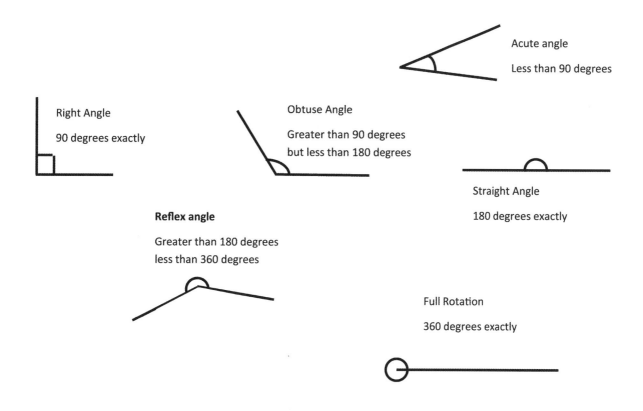

Name of Angle	Properties of Angle
Acute Angle	Greater than 0 degrees less than 90 degrees
Right Angle	Equal to 90 degrees

Check your chart solution with your teacher.

Now turn this angle information into a program that tells the user what an angle is when they type in the size in degrees.

Notes

Notes

Notes